JOURNEY TO
BETHLEHEM

Written by Akiko Kageyama

Illustrated by Taro Semba

JUDSON PRESS® VALLEY FORGE

One cold winter's night
many years ago, two shepherds
were watching their sheep when
they noticed a strange light
in the sky. It was brighter
than any star they had ever seen.

As the shepherds and their sheep gazed up
at the brightness in the sky,
an angel appeared above them.
The shepherds were very frightened, but
the angel said, "Do not be afraid. I have
wonderful news for you. A king has been
born in a stable in Bethlehem to bring
peace and love to all the world.
Hurry there
and see him.
This star
will show you
the way."

Suddenly, the sky was full of angels singing and playing music to celebrate the birth of their king. The shepherds and the sheep could hardly believe their eyes.

The shepherds did as the angel told them
and set off towards the town of Bethlehem.
"But there must be fifty stables
in Bethlehem," grumbled one of them.
"We'll never find him."
"Of course we will," answered the other.
"The angel told us to . . .

... follow the star."
The shepherds looked up
and there it was, still
moving on in front of them.

When they reached Bethlehem, the star
stopped above a very ordinary stable.
"Here we are," said the first shepherd.
"We'll never find a king in there!"
exclaimed the other.
"We won't if we don't look," his friend
replied, and he walked into the stable.

Inside, they found Mary and Joseph beside a manger
full of hay. In the manger lay a baby boy.
"Is this the king who will bring peace and love to
all the world?" the shepherds asked.
"Yes, this is Jesus, the son of God," answered Joseph.
The shepherds, the sheep and all the other animals
in the stable gazed at the baby king in wonder.

On their way home,
the shepherds told everyone they met
about the angels and the baby king.

Far off, in other lands,
three foreign kings had also seen
the moving star. They believed it would
lead them to a greater king than any
the world had ever known. They decided
to follow it and to take him presents.

When the three kings arrived
at the stable, Mary and Joseph
were very surprised.

The kings explained how they had followed
the star. Then they gave their presents
to Mary and Joseph for Jesus.
That night, an angel warned them in a dream
not to tell the king of that country about Jesus.
"He will be angry and jealous," said
the angel, "and will try to harm Jesus
if he can. He does not want anyone to be
greater than he is."

So the three kings went away in secret, but when they thought it was safe, they told everyone about the baby.

Through all the years since then, people have worshipped Jesus for the peace and love and courage he brings to those who believe in him.

Today, people all over the world
still worship Jesus. Every year,
on Christmas Day, his birthday,
people give each other presents.
These presents remind them of
the gift of peace and love
which the baby boy in the stable
brought to the world.

© Shiko-Sha Co., Ltd., Tokyo, 1978
© Text, Macdonald & Jane's Publishers, Ltd., 1979
First published in the U.S.A. in 1983 by Judson Press, Valley Forge, PA 19482-0851
Second printing, 1984
Printed in Japan
ISBN 0-8170-1012-2
The name JUDSON PRESS is registered in the U.S. Patent Office.